I SMELL A POP QUIZ!

A BIG NATE BOOK

by Lincoln Peirce

SCHOLASTIC INC.
New York Toronto London Auckland
Sydney Mexico City New Delhi Hong Kong

ISBN 978-0-545-44329-6

Big Nate copyright © by Newspaper Enterprise Association, Inc.
I Smell a Pop Quiz! copyright © 2008 by Newspaper Enterprise Association, Inc. All rights reserved. Published by Scholastic Inc., 557 Broadway, New York, NY 10012, by arrangement with United Feature Syndicate. SCHOLASTIC and associated logos are trademarks and/or registered trademarks of Scholastic Inc.

12 11 10 9 8 7 6 5 4 3 2 1   12 13 14 15 16 17/0

Printed in the U.S.A.   23

First Scholastic printing, January 2012

I DON'T REALLY GET LABOR DAY. WHAT'S THE POINT?

WHAT'S THE **POINT**? IT'S A GREAT HOLIDAY!

IT'S A CELEBRATION OF THE WORKERS THAT MAKE THIS COUNTRY GREAT! THE BUILDERS! THE PLUMBERS! THE TRUCK DRIVERS!...

...AAAAAANNNNND!...

DON'T SAY IT. DON'T SAY IT!

...THE SCHOOL TEACHERS!

YAAH!

When school let out,
What did they do?
Can you perhaps recall?

They shook your hand,
They smiled and said:
"We'll see you kids next fall!"

But fall,
Unless my eyes deceive,
Is sixteen days away.

SEPTEMBER

How come we're hearing
"Welcome back"
On such a summer day?

PRINCIPAL NICHOLS, WHAT'S WITH THE **HALL-WAY**?

WE HAD ALL THE CORRIDORS REPAINTED!

RESEARCH HAS SHOWN THAT **COLORS** CAN AFFECT **MOOD**! SO WE...

WHOA, **WHOA**! "RESEARCH HAS SHOWN"?

WHAT DOES **THAT** MEAN? A FEW **LAB RATS** LOOK AT SOME **COLOR SWATCHES**, AND ALL OF A SUDDEN WE'VE GOT **PINK WALLS**?

SO MUCH FOR THE SOOTHING PROPERTIES OF "OCEAN CORAL."

IF YOU WANT TO SPEND **MONEY**, HOW ABOUT BUMPING UP THE **FIELD TRIP** BUDGET?

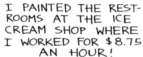

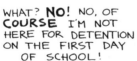

9

THERE ARE LEADERS, AND THERE ARE FOLLOWERS.

YOU DON'T SAY.

I'M A LEADER! **YOU'RE** A FOLLOWER!

HOLD IT, HOLD IT! WHY AM **I** A FOLLOWER?

WELL, JUST **LOOK** AT US, FRANCIS! WE'RE WALKING DOWN THE STREET, RIGHT?

YEAH. SO?

SO, **I'M** LEADING! **YOU'RE** FOLLOWING ME!

I'M THE ONE WHO DECIDES WHERE WE GO!

IF **YOU** WERE A LEADER, **YOU'D** BE IN FRONT! **YOU'D** BE DECIDING WHERE WE'RE GOING!

DO YOU... ☆CHUCKLE!☆ ...**FOLLOW** ME?

FRANCIS?

HEY, WAIT UP.

© 2006 by NEA, Inc.

11

COACH, I'M READY FOR ANOTHER GREAT SOCCER SEASON!

GLAD TO HEAR IT, NATE!

I'M GOING TO BE AN **IRON CURTAIN** THIS YEAR! I'M NOT GOING TO LET IN A **SINGLE GOAL!**

ASSUMING, OF COURSE, THAT YOU WIN THE JOB!

WIN THE JOB? WHY **WOULDN'T** I WIN THE JOB? I'VE **ALWAYS** BEEN THE GOALIE!

WELL, THIS YEAR YOU'VE GOT SOME COMPETITION!

HALLO, BACKSTOP COMRADE!

ARTUR!

© 2005 by NEA, Inc.

Peirce

WHOA, ARTUR, **WHOA!** WHAT'S GOING ON HERE?

AM TRYING OUT FOR TEAM!

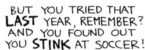
BUT YOU TRIED THAT **LAST** YEAR, REMEMBER? AND YOU FOUND OUT YOU **STINK** AT SOCCER!

YES! WHEN I TRY TO **SCORE** THE BALL, I STINK!

SO COACH MADE SUGGESTION FOR ME TO INSTEAD TRY TO **SAVING** BALL!

COACH DID?

© 2005 by NEA, Inc.

COACH DID??

...WHICH MAY NOT BE THE BRIGHTEST IDEA COACH HAS EVER HAD.

Peirce

COACH! HOW COME YOU TOLD **ARTUR** HE COULD TRY OUT FOR **GOALIE?**

WELL, WHY **SHOULDN'T** HE?

BECAUSE **I'M** OUR GOALIE!

YES! AND YOU'RE AN **EXCELLENT** ONE!

...WHICH IS WHY **ARTUR** PLAYING ALONGSIDE YOU IS SUCH A GOOD THING! HE HAS SO MUCH TO **LEARN** FROM YOU!

9/21

OH. UH... RIGHT!

BEFORE I SWITCHED TO PHYS. ED., I WAS A PSYCH MAJOR.

Peirce

© 2005 by NEA, Inc.

MR. EUSTIS, I'M HERE TO TELL YOU I'M GETTING OUT OF THE LAWN-MOWING BUSINESS.

I'M BURNED OUT, YOU KNOW WHAT I MEAN? THE GRIND IS JUST WEARING ME DOWN!

ANYWAY, SINCE YOU'RE ONE OF MY BEST CUSTOMERS, I JUST THOUGHT I'D LET YOU KNOW.

BUT YOU'RE ONLY **HALFWAY THROUGH MY LAWN!!**

AS I SAID, I'M BURNED OUT.

I'M BACK!

"BACK"? WERE YOU AWAY?

YES, I WAS AWAY! I WAS OUT BUYING OUR **HALLOWEEN TREATS!**

WHOA, WHOA. "TREATS"?

YOU DIDN'T SAY "CANDY"! AT HALLOWEEN YOU DON'T BUY **TREATS**, YOU BUY **CANDY!** YOU **DID**, DIDN'T YOU, DAD? YOU BOUGHT CANDY?

10/24

© 2005 by NEA, Inc.

SAY CANDY! SAY CANDY!

THE HEALTH FOOD STORE WAS MOBBED!

WHOA, DAD! **WHOA! WHOA!**

WHOA WHAT?

YOU BOUGHT OUR HALLOWEEN STUFF AT THE **HEALTH FOOD STORE!** YOU'RE GOING TO GIVE OUT **RICE CAKES** AGAIN!

NO I'M NOT!

THE STORE WAS **OUT** OF RICE CAKES! BUT NOT TO WORRY! I **LUCKED OUT!**

10/25

© 2005 by NEA, Inc.

DEFINE "LUCK."

I GOT THE **LAST THREE BAGS** OF DRIED APRICOTS!

DAD, **NO!** YOU'RE NOT GOING TO GIVE OUT **DRIED APRICOTS** FOR HALLOWEEN!

YOU'LL MAKE US A NEIGHBORHOOD **LAUGHINGSTOCK!**

RELAX, NATE! I WON'T GIVE OUT **ONLY** DRIED APRICOTS!

I'LL MIX IN SOME GRANOLA AND SUNFLOWER SEEDS AND MAKE LITTLE BAGGIES OF TRAIL MIX!

10/26

© 2005 by NEA, Inc.

WELL, PACK SOME FOR ME, BECAUSE I'M RUNNING AWAY FROM HOME.

...AND CRAISINS! I'LL ADD CRAISINS!

by Lincoln Peirce

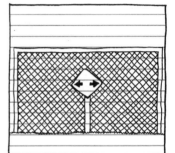

24

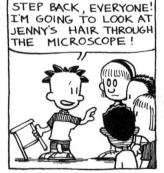

27

HEY! WHERE'S MRS. OLNEY?

OUT FOR THE WEEK! I'M MR. HANEY, THE SUBSTITUTE MUSIC TEACHER!

OH **HO!** A SUBSTITUTE, EH? HEY, ARE YOU A **COOL** SUB, LIKE THE GUY IN "SCHOOL OF ROCK"?

THE "SCHOOL OF ROCK"? I'M NOT FAMILIAR WITH THAT ONE.

MEET THE NEW BOSS, SAME AS THE OLD BOSS.

IS THAT THE ONE OVER BY "PIZZA HUT"?

SINCE YOU'RE A SUB, MR. HANEY, I CAN HELP YOU TAKE ATTENDANCE!

WELL, THANK YOU, UH...UM...

NATE!

NATE. OKAY, NATE, LET ME FIND YOU ON THE CLASS ROSTER...

OH.

I'VE GOT MY OWN FOLDER? COOL!

OKAY, GANG, TURN TO "RED RIVER VALLEY"...

AGAIN? WE PRACTICE THAT SONG **EVERY** DAY!

NATE, I'M SIMPLY FOLLOWING THE INSTRUCTIONS MRS. OLNEY LEFT FOR ME.

✲GRUMBLE!✲ MRS. OLNEY NEVER LETS US TRY ANYTHING NEW.

I MEAN, I KEEP ASKING HER IF WE CAN START A MARCHING BAND, BUT SHE...

SLAM!

CALL ME CRAZY, BUT I DON'T THINK YOU'RE READY FOR A MARCHING BAND JUST YET.

OOPSY.

29

the FIVE STAGES of TEST-TAKING

1. SHOCK

CLEAR YOUR DESKS, PEOPLE.

POINK!

2. DENIAL

...BUT YOU TOLD US THE TEST WAS **TOMORROW!** DIDN'T SHE, GUYS? DIDN'T SHE SAY THE TEST WAS TOMORROW? I DISTINCTLY REMEMBER YOU SAYING THAT...

3. ANGER

OH, HOW I HATE HER.

4. QUESTIONING

Q: What was the significance of the adoption and subsequent ratification of the Articles of Confederation in 1777?

5. ACCEPTANCE

A: I have no idea.

SIGH...

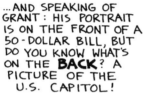

GINA, I'VE COME UP WITH A NEW COMIC STRIP FOR THE NEWSPAPER! TAKE A LOOK!

"MRS. GOSLEY"?

THE HILARIOUS ADVENTURES OF A SADISTIC SIXTH-GRADE TEACHER!

IS THIS BASED ON ANYBODY WE KNOW?

DEFINE "BASED ON."

IS THIS MRS. GODFREY?

DEFINE "IS".

NATE, ARE YOU OUT OF YOUR **MIND**? WE CAN'T PRINT THIS COMIC STRIP IN THE NEWSPAPER! WE'LL GET **EXPELLED**!

WHY?

BECAUSE THIS "MRS. GOSLEY" CHARACTER IS SO CLEARLY BASED ON **MRS. GODFREY**!

WHAT? SHE IS **NOT**!

THERE ARE **MANY** DIFFERENCES! I MEAN, MRS. GODFREY IS A SIXTH GRADE SOCIAL STUDIES TEACHER!

MRS. **GOSLEY** TEACHES **MATH**!

RIGHT. STOP THE PRESSES.

LET ME GET THIS STRAIGHT, GINA: YOU WON'T PRINT MY COMIC STRIP?

YOUR COMIC STRIP ATTACKING MRS. GODFREY? NO, I **WON'T**!

THIS IS **CENSORSHIP**! "MRS. GOSLEY" DESERVES TO BE **SEEN**!

YOU THINK SO?

WELL, HERE COMES MRS. GODFREY. LET **HER** SEE IT.

RIP RIP RIP RIP RIP RIP RIP RIP RIP RIP

40

NATE! WE JUST HAD OUR FIRST CHESS MEETING! WHERE WERE YOU?

I'VE DECIDED NOT TO PLAY THIS YEAR.

I REALLY HAVE NOTHING LEFT TO PROVE. I'VE ACCOMPLISHED EVERYTHING I WANT TO IN CHESS.

YOU'VE NEVER BEATEN ARTUR.

HNGK!

...EXCEPT THAT TIME HE **LET** YOU WIN!

NASTY LITTLE FACIAL TIC YOU'VE GOT THERE!

BLINK BLINK BLINK

OKAY, YOU GUYS ARE RIGHT. I ADMIT THAT THE FACT I'VE NEVER BEATEN ARTUR AT CHESS STICKS IN MY CRAW.

IT'S THE ONE THING IN MY LIFE I HAVEN'T SUCCEEDED AT.

"THE ONE THING"?

MMPH!

SHUT UP.

SO YESTERDAY'S MATH TEST DOESN'T COUNT?

MR. ROSA, I WASN'T GOING TO PLAY CHESS THIS YEAR, BUT I'VE CHANGED MY MIND.

GREAT! WE NEED YOU!

WITH ARTUR PLAYING FIRST BOARD AND YOU AT NUMBER TWO, WE SHOULD...

DON'T BE SO SURE IT'LL BE **ARTUR** PLAYING FIRST BOARD!

I INTEND TO **CHALLENGE** ARTUR FOR FIRST BOARD AND **CRUSH** HIM LIKE A... LIKE A...

AS I WAS SAYING... WE SHOULD BE A GOOD **TEAM.**

YEAH, WHATEVER. HELP ME THINK OF SOMETHING CRUSHABLE.

46

47

www.comics.com

© 2005 by NEA, Inc.

53

AHEM, DAD! DO YOU **MIND**?

HM?

THAT'S **MY** ISSUE OF "FEMME FATALITY"! YOU **PINCHED** IT WHILE I WAS IN THE BATHROOM!

YOU'RE RIGHT. I ADMIT IT.

...BUT JUST GIVE ME FIVE MORE MINUTES! OKAY? I'M ALMOST DONE! I'VE ONLY GOT FOUR PAGES TO GO!

I'M AT THE PART WHERE FEMME ESCAPES FROM THE...

DON'T TELL ME!! DON'T TELL ME!

OKAY, DAD, I'LL GIVE YOU **TWO MINUTES** TO FINISH MY "FEMME FATALITY"... BUT THEN I WANT IT **BACK!**

OKAY.

SIIGHH...

OOOOH!

HUBBA HUBBA!

DAD, YOU'RE CREEPING ME OUT.

TIME'S UP, DAD. HAND OVER THE COMIC BOOK.

BUT I'M NOT DONE WITH MY "FEMME FATALITY"!

YOUR "FEMME FATAL-ITY"? ex**CUSE** ME, DAD, BUT SHE'S **MY** "FEMME FATALITY"! SHE'S **MY** CRUSH!

YOU CAN SETTLE FOR OGLING THE MODELS IN THIS "EDDIE BAUER" CATALOG.

IT'S NOT REALLY MUCH FUN LOOKING AT THE WINTER ISSUE.

MAN, WHAT A DAY.

REALLY? WELL, THERE'S A SURPRISE IN YOUR BEDROOM!

AN OLD FRIEND IS WAITING FOR YOU IN THERE!

REALLY? WOW!

YARRRGH!

WERE YOU REFERRING TO SPITSY, OR TO THE RECURRENCE OF HIS "IRRITABLE BOWEL SYNDROME"?

WURF!

MR. EUSTIS IS VISITING HIS SISTER IN FLORIDA, SO SPITSY WILL BE WITH US ALL WEEK.

ALL WEEK? COOL!

A WEEK SHOULD BE PLENTY OF TIME FOR ME TO WORK MY TRANSFORMATION!

TRANSFORMATION? OF WHAT?

OF SPITSY, DAD! I'M GOING TO MAKE HIM INTO A REAL DOG! A DOG WHO CHASES CATS! A DOG WHO FETCHES STICKS!

...A DOG WHO DOESN'T WATCH "THAT'S SO RAVEN"!

WURF!

YOU GO, GIRL!

OKAY, SPITSY, TIME TO GET TO WORK! TIME TO TURN YOU INTO A REAL DOG!

HERE. MR. EUSTIS LEFT YOU THIS LIST OF SPITSY FACTS TO HELP YOU WITH YOUR DOG-SITTING.

"SPITSY CANNOT FALL ASLEEP UNLESS HE IS LISTENING TO THE STIRRING VOCALS OF POP SUPERSTAR CLAY AIKEN."

BAD DOG. BAAAAAD, BAD, BAD, BAD, BAD, BAD, BAD DOG.

WURF!

58

GREETINGS, GENTS! MY CARD!

YOUR CARD?

I CAN'T EVEN **READ** THIS! WHAT'S IT SAY?

"NATE WRIGHT, LIFE SKILLS COACH"!

DOES IRONY COUNT AS A LIFE SKILL?

CAN'T TALK NOW! I'M ON MY WAY TO DETENTION!

HOW DID **YOU**, OF ALL PEOPLE, DECIDE TO BECOME A **LIFE SKILLS COACH**?

I SAW A NEED, THAT'S ALL!

THIS SCHOOL IS FULL OF KIDS WHO NEED MY HELP! KIDS WHO HAVE NO SOCIAL SKILLS WHATSOEVER!

YOU'D BE **SHOCKED** TO LEARN HOW MANY KIDS THERE ARE AROUND HERE WHO ARE UTTERLY **CLUELESS!**

LESS SHOCKED THAN YOU'D THINK.

HEEEEY, BABY, GOT ANY FRIES TO GO WITH THAT SHAKE?

GREETINGS, FRIENDS! NATE WRIGHT, LIFE SKILLS COACH, AT YOUR SERVICE!

FOR A VERY REASON-ABLE FEE, I CAN HELP YOU ACQUIRE THE TOOLS YOU NEED TO WIN AT THE GAME OF LIFE!

NO PROBLEM CAN'T BE SOLVED! NO OBSTACLE CAN'T BE SURMOUNTED! IT'S ALL ABOUT BEING A CAN-DO PERSON AND HAVING A POSITIVE ATTITUDE!

AREN'T YOU THE KID WHO BURNED OFF HIS EYEBROWS IN SCIENCE LAB?

SEE, RIGHT THERE. THAT'S WAY TOO NEGATIVE.

Dear friend, I mean not to alarm
Or do your disposition harm.
But all around us, near and far,
Lurk creatures gruesome and bizarre.

You may not even be aware
(Indeed, some folks seem not to care!)
That such foul beasts, such monsters rank
Reside in shadows dark and dank.

They lie in wait, they slink, they creep,
Prepared to pounce, to lunge, to leap,
To sink their claws into your flesh,
To feast anew on victims fresh.

And even when they hide away,
A stench their presence does betray:
A rancid stink, a bilious scent,
Foreshadowing their ill intent.

My friend, don't think yourself immune!
Your Day of Judgment's coming soon.
You'll sense the creature drawing near,
And turn to run, in abject fear.

By then, though, it will be too late.
A close encounter is your fate.
Your screams of terror will not matter...

DON'T JUST STAND THERE! GET A LADDER!

65

WOW. I'VE NEVER SEEN MR. ROSA SO MAD. HE WENT **OFF**.

I'VE SEEN THIS BEFORE. HE'S BURNED OUT.

HE NEVER SMILES ANYMORE, HE YELLS AT US FOR NO REASON, AND HE'S NEGLECTING HIS PERSONAL GROOMING.

HE'S GOT THE CLASSIC SYMPTOMS.

HUH.

BUT WAIT. **ALL** THE TEACHERS ARE LIKE THAT.

AS I SAID, I'VE SEEN THIS BEFORE.

MR. ROSA, ALL THE KIDS HAVE NOTICED HOW CRABBY YOU'VE BEEN LATELY. YOU'RE OBVIOUSLY SUFFERING FROM BURNOUT.

WELL, TEDDY AND I DON'T WANT TO INCREASE YOUR STRESS LEVEL. WE DON'T WANT TO CONTRIBUTE TO THE BURNOUT PHENOMENON.

WELL, THAT'S VERY NICE OF...

... SO WE'LL BE OVER THERE, PLAYING TABLE FOOTBALL.

WEIRD. NOW HE LOOKS **MORE** STRESSED.

NOT OUR PROBLEM, DUDE. WE'VE DONE **OUR** PART.

WHAT'S GOING ON OVER HERE?

WE'RE PLAYING TABLE FOOTBALL!

NATE, FLICKING A PAPER TRIANGLE ACROSS A TABLE IS NOT AN ACCEPTABLE USE OF YOUR CLASS TIME.

YOU KNOW, YOU'RE RIGHT. THIS TABLE ISN'T REALLY BIG ENOUGH.

LET'S PLAY "HANGMAN"!

DETE_TIO_

"N."

BINGO.

BOYS, THE PRINCIPAL WILL SEE YOU NOW.

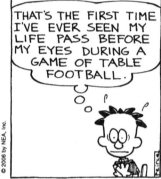

by Lincoln Peirce

REMEMBER! TODAY IS PAJAMA DAY!

NICE P.J.'S, TEDDY!

YOU TOO!

SHARP JAMMIES, MR. GALVIN!

THANKS, GENTS!

HEY! MRS. GODFREY! YOU'RE NOT WEARING PAJAMAS!

YES, I KNOW.

BUT IT'S PAJAMA DAY!

I DON'T OWN ANY PAJAMAS. I DON'T WEAR THEM.

YOU DON'T?

THEN WHAT DO YOU SLEEP IN?

© 2006 by NEA, Inc.

NOTHING.

QUICK, START TALKING ABOUT SOMETHING ELSE.

I MAY NEVER SLEEP AGAIN.

MR. ROSA, DO YOU THINK IT'S WRONG TO WANT TO BE FAMOUS?

WRONG? WELL, I...

FRANCIS AND TEDDY THINK I'M **SHALLOW** FOR WANTING TO BE FAMOUS!

...BUT WHAT'S **WRONG** WITH IT? I MEAN, ALL I WANT IS TO BE **KNOWN**! TO BE **TALKED** ABOUT!

© 2006 by NEA, Inc.

IF IT MAKES YOU FEEL ANY BETTER, YOU'RE ALREADY SOMETHING OF A LEGEND IN THE FACULTY LOUNGE.

I AM?

Peirce

THREE PAGES ON THE BOSTON TEA PARTY! HOW AM I GONNA WRITE THREE WHOLE PAGES ON THE BOSTON TEA PARTY?

PERSONALLY, I'M NOT **GOING** TO WRITE THREE PAGES!

WHAT DO YOU MEAN?

I'M GOING TO WRITE **ONE** PAGE, THEN **TURN IT INTO** THREE!

HOW ARE YOU GONNA MANAGE THAT?

ONE WORD, TEDDY: **FONT SIZE!**

THAT'S TWO WORDS, NIMROD.

I'LL GO WITH A TIMES ROMAN TWENTY-FOUR! NO, TWENTY-**EIGHT!**

TICKA TICKA TIK TIK TAK

4/17

OBSERVE, TEDDY, AS I DEMONSTRATE THE TRANSFORMATIVE POWER OF **FONTS!**

GODFREY SAID WE HAD TO TYPE THESE USING A 14-POINT FONT, RIGHT? WELL, **BOTH** OF THESE ARE 14-POINT FONTS!

TIKKA TAKKA TIK TIKKITY TAK TIK

4/18

The Boston Tea Party, which took place on December 16, 1773, was a very significant event in United States history.

The Boston Tea Party, which took place on December 16, 1773, was a very significant event in United States history.

IT... IT'S A **MIRACLE!**

AMEN, BROTHER!

TIKKA TIKKA TIK TAK

TEDDY, YOU'RE NEVER GONNA MAKE IT TO THREE PAGES LIKE **THAT!**

WHAT DO YOU MEAN, "LIKE THAT"?

YOU CAN'T JUST WRITE "THE COLONISTS WERE MAD AT ENGLAND FOR TAXING THEIR TEA"! THAT'S TOO **SHORT!** YOU'VE GOT TO STRETCH IT **OUT!**

To say the colonists were upset with England for taxing their tea is understating the matter. They were BEYOND upset. They were angry, irate, miffed, peeved, mad, furious, perturbed, enraged, ticked off, sore, chafed, cross, huffy, incensed, and generally splenetic.

TIK TAK TIK TIK

4/19

"SPLENETIC"?

Or, to put it another way,

...AND FOR NUMBER NINE, I PUT "C."

YUP! ME TOO!

...AND FOR NUMBER TEN, I PUT "A."

"A"?

WELL, IT OBVIOUSLY WASN'T "B" OR "C."

I KNOW. I PUT "D."

REALLY? I'M PRETTY SURE IT WAS "A," FRANCIS.

NO, I THINK IT WAS "D."

WELL, THERE'S ONE PERSON WHO CAN SETTLE THIS.

YOU'RE RIGHT!

NATE! ON THE MATH TEST, WHAT'D YOU PUT FOR NUMBER TEN?

"A."

ARE YOU POSITIVE?

YEAH. THAT WAS AN EASY ONE.

DANG.

DUDE, YOU'RE LIKE AN ANTI-ANSWER KEY.

HUH?

Panel 1: OH, NO! / WHAT'S **THIS**, GINA? DO I DETECT A NOTE OF **DIS-APPOINTMENT** IN YOUR VOICE?

Panel 2: FOR ONCE IN YOUR LIFE, DID YOU GET **LESS** THAN A PERFECT SCORE ON A TEST? / YES.

Panel 3: OOOOH! SPILL IT, GINA! WHAT'D YOU GET? A 90?... AN 85?... MAYBE EVEN AN **80**? / A 109.

Panel 4: I HAD A SPELLING ERROR ON THE EXTRA CREDIT. / OH, HOW I HATE HER.

Panel 5: YOU GOT AN "A" ON THE SCIENCE TEST? / YOU'RE **AMAZING**, GINA! / *GRUMBLE*

Panel 6: DOESN'T IT MAKE YOU **SICK**? GINA'S ON HER WAY TO WINNING YET **ANOTHER** "OUTSTANDING SCHOLAR" MEDAL! / MAYBE NOT...

Panel 7: MAYBE SOMEONE **ELSE** WILL WIN THIS YEAR. / BUT **WHO**? WHO COULD POSSIBLY COMPETE WITH **GINA**?

Panel 8: YOU GOT AN "A-PLUS" ON THE SCIENCE TEST? / YOU'RE **AMAZING**, FRANCIS! / **KA-BOING!**

Panel 9: FRANCIS! **YOU'RE** SMART ENOUGH! **YOU** COULD DO IT! / I COULD DO WHAT?

Panel 10: YOU COULD WIN THE "OUTSTANDING SCHOLAR" MEDAL INSTEAD OF **GINA**! YOU'VE GOT THE BRAINS TO TAKE HER DOWN! YOU'RE **BRILLIANT**! / BRILLIANT?

Panel 11: BUT YOU ALWAYS **BUST** ON ME FOR HAVING BRAINS! / **BUST** ON YOU? I DON'T **BUST** ON YOU! TEDDY, DO I **BUST** ON FRANCIS?

Panel 12: UHH... / "PENCIL NECK POIN-DEXTER" ISN'T A **BUST**? / IT'S AN AFFECTIONATE NICKNAME!

IT'S ALL GOING TO COME DOWN TO THE SCIENCE FINAL, FRANCIS! IF YOU SCORE TWELVE POINTS HIGHER THAN **GINA**...

...THEN **YOU'LL** WIN THE "OUTSTANDING SCHOLAR" MEDAL!

FORGET IT, NATE! **NO**BODY CAN OUTSCORE GINA BY TWELVE POINTS!

WHAT? FRANCIS, YOU CAN'T THINK SO **NEGATIVELY!** DO YOU THINK LOUIS PASTEUR HAD THOUGHTS LIKE THAT BEFORE HE INVENTED MILK?

NO, I'M PRETTY SURE HE DIDN'T.

WELL, THEN. LET THAT BE A LESSON TO YOU.

SO LONG, DAD! I'M GOING OVER TO FRANCIS'S HOUSE FOR A STUDY SESSION!

GREAT!

I'M GLAD TO SEE YOU'RE GETTING READY FOR YOUR FINALS!

OH, WE'LL BE READY, ALL RIGHT!

...READY TO KNOCK THAT BRAINIAC **GINA** OFF HER PEDESTAL FOR ONCE IN HER SNOBBY, "I'M SMARTER THAN YOU ARE" **LIFE!**

STUDYING HAS CHANGED A BIT SINCE I WAS A BOY.

BWA HA HA HA HAA!

MR. GALVIN, WHAT'S THE SCIENCE FINAL GOING TO BE LIKE? WILL IT BE HARD, OR EASY, OR...

OH, IT SHOULD PROVIDE A NICE CHALLENGE.

WORRIED ABOUT HOW YOU'LL DO?

HM? NO, I'M WORRIED ABOUT HOW **FRANCIS** WILL DO!

I COULDN'T CARE LESS ABOUT HOW **I'LL** DO!

I'D SAY THAT PRETTY MUCH SUMS IT UP.

HEY, CAN YOU GIVE GINA A HARDER TEST THAN EVERYBODY ELSE?

98

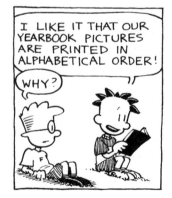

AH, THE COUNTY FAIR!

COME ON, GUYS! LET'S START OUR SEARCH FOR THE WILDEST RIDE!

AND HOW DO WE FIGURE OUT WHICH RIDE IS THE WILDEST?

IT'S EASY! YOU LOOK FOR THE CRAZIEST-LOOKING OPERATOR!

THE MORE DERANGED THE OPERATOR LOOKS, THE WILDER THE RIDE! IT'S A PROVEN **FACT!**

SPEAKING OF DERANGED...

OOH! GUYS! JACKPOT!

RIDE the GUT CHECK!

5 tickets

AH! JENNY, M'LADY!

EWWW! NATE, THAT'S **GROSS!**

WHAT'S GROSS?

YOUR **SHIRT!** YOU GOT **MOTION SICK** ON ONE OF THE RIDES!

NO, I DIDN'T! I HAVEN'T EVEN **GONE** ON ANY RIDES YET!

HE'S JUST A SLOB!

LOOK, IS IT **MY** FAULT THEY OVER-STUFFED MY CHILI DOG?

HEY, MAN, IS THIS RIDE SCARY?

RIDE BLACK HOLE 4 TIX!

HELLO? **MISTER!**

HM? OH, SORRY, KID.

BLACK HOLE

I WEAR EARPLUGS SO I CAN'T HEAR THE **SCREAMS** OF **TERROR!**

"MAKE IT STOP!"..."LET ME OFF!" I MEAN, WHO WANTS TO LISTEN TO **THAT** ALL DAY?

TWO, PLEASE!

YES! RIGHT DOWN THE....

...MIDDLE.

..IF BY "MIDDLE" YOU MEAN THE MEDIAN STRIP OF ROUTE 95.

MULLIGAN.

...AND IT'S IN THE CUP! WHAT'D I TAKE ON THIS HOLE?

UH...THAT DEPENDS..

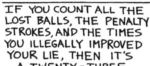
IF YOU COUNT ALL THE LOST BALLS, THE PENALTY STROKES, AND THE TIMES YOU ILLEGALLY IMPROVED YOUR LIE, THEN IT'S A TWENTY-THREE.

IF, ON THE OTHER HAND, YOU COMPLETELY DIS-REGARD THE RULES OF GOLF, THEN IT'S A FIVE.

LET'S SPLIT THE DIFFERENCE AND CALL IT A SIX!

THAT SEEMS FAIR.

HOW COME EVERYBODY CHEATS AT GOLF?

I MEAN, YOU DON'T SEE PEOPLE CHEAT-ING AT BOWLING!

WELL, YOU CAN'T CHEAT AT BOWLING, NOW THAT ALL THE ALLEYS HAVE ELEC-TRONIC SCORING!

BACK WHEN PEOPLE KEPT SCORE WITH A PENCIL AND PAPER, IT WAS **EASY** TO CHEAT!

GREAT, DAD. NICE ROLE MODELING.

OOP! GET OUT OF THE ROUGH, YOU RASCAL!

KICK!

107

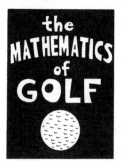

AH, **PETER**! READY FOR YOUR FIRST DAY OF "CAMP NATE"?

I'M AFRAID SHO.

OH, C'MON NOW! WE'RE GOING TO HAVE **FUN**! WE'LL PLAY FRISBEE GOLF, GO ON A NATURE HIKE, MAYBE CLIMB A FEW TREES...

FIRSHT I'VE BEEN INSHTRUCTED TO GIVE YOU THISH NOTE FROM MY MOTHER.

DEAR CAMP STAFF: PETER IS ALLERGIC TO MOST AIRBORNE PARTICULATES, MUST APPLY SUNBLOCK EVERY TEN MINUTES, AND HAS A BLADDER THE SIZE OF A MALIBU BARBIE LATTE CUP.

THIS IS TAKING FULL DISCLOSURE A BIT TOO FAR.

WHICH REMINDSH ME: WHERE'SH THE BATHROOM?

OKAY, PETER, LET'S GET THIS SUMMER CAMP STARTED! WHAT WOULD YOU LIKE TO DO FIRST?

WHAT WOULD **I** LIKE TO DO FIRSHT?

YOU TELL **ME**! **YOU'RE** SHUPPOSHED TO BE THE ONE TO PLAN ALL THE FUN ACTIVITIESH!!

UH... RIGHT. OKAY, THEN...

OUR FIRST ACTIVITY IS A LITTLE GAME I LIKE TO CALLLL...

..."GUESS THE NAME OF OUR **SECOND** ACTIVITY"!

DOESH YAWNING QUALIFY AS AN ACTIVITY?

OKAY, PETER. NEXT UP ON OUR SCHEDULE: A **WILDLIFE WALK**!

WILDLIFE WALK?

THISH ISH **SHUBURBIA**! WHAT KINDSH OF WILDLIFE ARE YOU EXSHPECTING TO SHEE?

OOP! LISTEN! I THINK I JUST HEARD A **COYOTE**!

WURF!

SHURELY YOU JESHT.

I THOUGHT WE AGREED YOU'D LOSE THE CONE AND SWEATER.

WAG WAG WAG WAG WAG WA WA

119

WITH ALL DUE RESHPECT, "CAMP NATE" HASHN'T EXACTLY BEEN SHCINTILLATING SHO FAR!

WELL, HOW ABOUT A SCAVENGER HUNT?

OOOH! A SHCAVENGER HUNT! **NOW** WE'RE TALKIN'!

HERE, YOU'LL NEED THIS CHECKLIST.

8/7

... AND MAKE SURE YOU READ IT **CAREFULLY**! YOU'VE GOT TO BRING BACK **EXACTLY** WHAT THE LIST SAYS!

TUNA MELT ON WHEAT, ORANGE SHODA, BAR-B-QUE CHIPSH...

CHOP CHOP! TIME'S-A-WASTIN'! GOT ANY CASH ON YOU?

CLAP CLAP CLAP

© 2006 by NEA, Inc.
Peirce

HEY, **I** KNOW WHAT WE CAN DO NEXT! LET'S SING CAMPFIRE SONGS!

CAMPFIRE SHONGSH?

IT'SH TEN-THIRTY IN THE MORNING, **AND** WE HAVE NO CAMPFIRE!

WHO CARES? LET'S JUST **PRETEND** WE HAVE ONE!

8/8

C'MON, PETER, GET WITH THE "CAMP NATE" SPIRIT! WHAT'S YOUR FAVORITE SONG?

WELL, I'M QUITE SHMITTEN WITH FREDERIC CHOPIN'SH "POLONAISHE NO. 6 IN A FLAT MAJOR".

UH... OKAY. YOU START.

© 2006 by NEA, Inc.
Peirce

FRANKLY, PETER, YOU DON'T SEEM TO BE ENJOYING THE "CAMP NATE" EXPERIENCE.

WHAT EXSHPER-IENCE?

8/9

THERE **ISH** NO "CAMP NATE" EXSHPERIENCE BECAUSHE THISH ISHN'T A REAL **CAMP**! IT'SH JUSHT **YOU AND ME**!

I **THOUGHT** YOU MIGHT SAY THAT!

... WHICH IS WHY I'D LIKE TO PRESENT YOU WITH THIS SPECIAL **T-SHIRT** TO HELP PUMP UP YOUR CAMP SPIRIT!

© 2006 by NEA, Inc.

"CHICAGO CUBS 2003 WORLD CHAMPS".

I'VE ALSO GOT A FEW BUFFALO BILLS SUPER BOWL SHIRTS!

Peirce

WELL, IT'SH ONE O'CLOCK, AND ALREADY WE'VE BLOWN THROUGH ALL THE LAME ACTIVITIESH YOU PLANNED FOR THE DAY!

MY MOTHER'SH NOT PICKING ME UP FOR THREE MORE HOURS! GOT ANY MORE BRIGHT IDEAS?

I SURE DO!

HERE. LET ME KNOW WHEN YOU'RE DONE.

THE NEW YORK TIMESH CROSSH-WORD PUZZLE?

NO COM-PLAINING. IT'S NOT LIKE IT'S THE SUNDAY EDITION.

WHAT'S UP WITH THIS?

I THOUGHT YOU WERE RUNNING "CAMP NATE"!

I AM!

I JUST GAVE PETER A PENCIL AND THE NEW YORK TIMES CROSSWORD PUZZLE!

WHAT? THE KID'S IN FIRST GRADE!

CHUCKLE!... EXACTLY! THAT THING'LL KEEP HIM BUSY ALL AFTER...

DONE.

...NOON.

THE PENCIL BROKE, SHO I USHED A "SHARPIE."

HELLO, MOTHER? I DEMAND YOU LEAVE WORK EARLY AND PICK ME UP THISH INSHTANT!

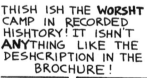

THISH ISH THE WORSHT CAMP IN RECORDED HISHTORY! IT ISHN'T ANYTHING LIKE THE DESHCRIPTION IN THE BROCHURE!

WHAT?...THE WATER SHPORTS? MOTHER, THE SHO-CALLED WATER SHPORTS ARE AN ABSHOLUTE FIASHCO!

WOULD YOU LIKE TO HEAR ABOUT THE WORLD'SH SHORTESHT GAME OF "MARCO POLO"?

YOUR TURN TO BE "IT."

 THERE ARE TWO KINDS OF PEOPLE IN THE WORLD. MEN AND WOMEN?

 DOG PEOPLE AND CAT PEOPLE! OH, BROTHER.

 IT'S **TRUE**! NOW, YOU: **YOU** LIKE **CATS**! BUT I ALSO LIKE DOGS!

 BUT YOU LIKE CATS **MORE**! THAT MAKES YOU A **CAT PERSON**! CAN'T I BE BOTH?

 **NO**, YOU CAN'T BE **BOTH**, FRANCIS! IT'S **EITHER-OR**! NO EXCEPTIONS! NO COMPROMISES!

 YOU'RE EITHER A DOG PERSON OR A CAT PERSON! THAT'S ALL THERE IS TO IT!

 WHAM!

 HOW DOGMATIC! KEEP IT UP, SPITSY, AND I JUST MIGHT SWITCH SIDES. PANT PANT PANT PANT PANT

HERE YOU GO, NATE. TWO SCOOPS OF MOCHA CHIP.

THAT'S IT?

WHAT DO YOU MEAN?

WELL, YOU'RE AN **ARTIST**, RIGHT? CAN'T YOU MAKE A CONE WITH A BIT MORE **PIZAZZ**? A BIT MORE **EXPRESSION**?

STICK A CHERRY ON THERE!... ADD SOME JIMMIES!... ASK YOURSELF: WHAT WOULD REMBRANDT HAVE DONE?

I'M PRETTY SURE REMBRANDT WOULDN'T HAVE FOUND HIMSELF WORKING A SUMMER JOB AT AN ICE CREAM SHOP CALLED "SWEET LICKS".

YOU'VE GOT TWO PRETTY COOL JOBS, MR. ROSA! YOU'RE AN ART TEACHER **AND** AN ICE CREAM GUY!

WHICH JOB DO YOU LIKE BETTER?

WHOOPS!

SPLUT!

DANG IT!

THEY'RE UNCANNILY SIMILAR.

THAT'LL BE $2.95 FOR THE CONE, NATE.

HERE YOU GO, MR. ROSA! KEEP THE CHANGE!

WOW. A FIVE-CENT TIP. NOW I CAN RETIRE.

RETIRE? RETIRE FROM **TEACHING**? HOLD ON, NOW, HOLD **ON**!

IF YOU RETIRE, THE SCHOOL WILL PROBABLY HIRE SOME TOTAL **IDIOT** TO TEACH ART! THAT CAN'T HAPPEN! I WON'T **LET** IT!!

YOU WANT YOUR NICKEL BACK, DON'T YOU?

ACTUALLY, COULD YOU MAKE IT A QUARTER? I WAS JUST NOTICING YOUR GUM-BALL MACHINE.